Clarinet Exam Pieces

ABRSM Grade 1

Selected from the 2018–2021 syllabus

Name

Date of exam 14.29
John St. Baptist Church
Strand

Contents

page

Consultant Editor for ABRSM: David Blackwell
Footnotes: Dominic Wells

Other pieces for Grade 1

First published in 2017 by ABRSM (Publishing) Ltd,
a wholly owned subsidiary of ABRSM, 4 London Wall Place,
London EC2Y 5AU, United Kingdom
© 2017 by The Associated Board of the Royal Schools of Music
Distributed worldwide by Oxford University Press

Music origination by Julia Bovee
Cover by Kate Benjamin & Andy Potts
Printed in England by Page Bros (Norwich) Ltd,
on materials from sustainable sources.

Daisy Bell

Arranged by Nancy Litten

Harry Dacre
(1857–1922)

Daisy Bell is a popular song, written in 1892 by the English composer Harry Dacre. It's also known as *Bicycle Built for Two*, since the final phrase (bars 28–end) sets the words 'but you'll look sweet, on the seat of a bicycle built for two'. When Dacre first visited America, he brought his bicycle with him, and had to pay import tax. A friend commented: 'It's lucky you didn't bring a bicycle built for two, otherwise you'd have to pay double duty!' Dacre was so taken with the phrase 'bicycle built for two' that he used it in the song. The music-hall style of the song implies a relaxed, informal manner and legato phrasing – as if singing.

© 2017 by The Associated Board of the Royal Schools of Music

Minuet

No. 2 from *Nannerl-Notenbuch*

A:2

Arranged by David Blackwell

Leopold Mozart
(1719–87)

This Minuet was written by Leopold Mozart, famous for his *Toy Symphony* and as the father of one of the most well-known composers of all time: Wolfgang Amadeus Mozart. Minuets were popular dances during the Classical period, so try to feel a dance-like quality when playing the piece. Like waltzes, minuets are always in triple time, and this particular example comes from the *Nannerl-Notenbuch*, a collection of pieces written for Wolfgang's sister, Nannerl. As well as writing music for them to perform, Leopold made sure his children practised very hard every day, which is why they both became such great musicians.

A:3

La Bourée

from *Terpsichore*

Arranged by Alan Bullard

Michael Praetorius
(1571–1621)

Michael Praetorius was one of the finest composers of the early German Baroque period. He is often associated with Protestant hymns, many of which he arranged – adding extra instrumental parts for grand religious ceremonies, such as Christmas. Today he is perhaps most famous for his collection of dance music called *Terpsichore*, named after the goddess of dance in ancient Greek mythology. It contains more than 300 instrumental dances, including this Bourée (here given its French spelling). The bourrée was a lively French dance in quick duple time, and in this example the dance character is emphasized by the contrasting dynamics.

Hush-a-bye

from *Playaround* for Clarinet, Book 1

 B:1

Roma Cafolla
(born 1949)

31.1.19

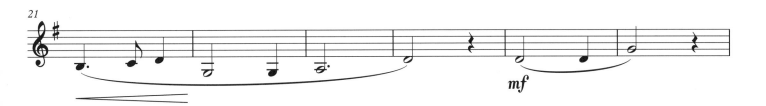

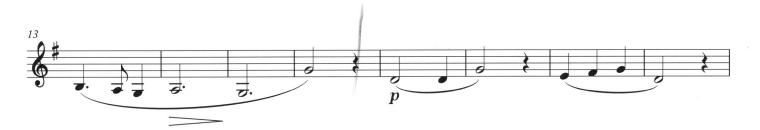

As well as its title, 'Hush-a-bye', a useful clue about how to play this piece appears right at the very beginning: legato. This is a lullaby, so imagine you're trying to send a baby off to sleep by playing with a nice, smooth (legato) line throughout. However, although it's a lullaby, it doesn't remain quiet the whole time. The dynamics gradually swell up and down: perhaps the baby is not quite comfortable enough and starting to stir in the louder sections. But you finally manage to soothe it with your playing, and send it back into a calm slumber.

Roma Cafolla is a Northern Irish composer. She is also a lyricist, adjudicator, pianist and cellist.

B:2

Sundown

from *In the Groove* for Clarinet

James Rae
(born 1957)

As you play this piece, try to imagine the golden sun fading away into night. The opening melody sets the scene, with the swung quavers creating a sense of relaxation. Quiet dynamic markings also add to the feeling of calm, only briefly rising to **mf**. Although the clarinet has the melody at the start while the piano accompanies, in bars 9–12 the roles are reversed: the piano takes the melody while the clarinet plays a supporting role, before returning with the theme in bar 13.

Having studied clarinet, bass clarinet, piano and composition at the Guildhall School of Music and Drama, James Rae has pursued a successful and varied career in music.

Little Brown Jug

B:3

Arranged by Nikki Iles

Joseph Winner
(1837–1918)

Joseph Winner wrote the song *Little Brown Jug* in 1869, and it remained well known as a folk song in the early 20th century. However, it became even more popular in 1939, when the famous bandleader Glenn Miller recorded and broadcast his instrumental arrangement of the song. The record was a great success, and went on to become one of the best-known orchestrations of the American Big Band era. One of the key elements of Big Band music is feeling a sense of swung rhythms, just as the quavers in this piece should be swung. It's fun music with a good sense of humour!

C:1

Early Doors

from *Jazz Club* Clarinet, Grades 1–2

Ned Bennett
(born 1966)

'Early Doors' is a British slang phrase referring to people who arrive somewhere earlier than normal. It originated in theatres in the 1800s, when customers who paid extra were allowed to enter the theatre early and choose their own seats before everyone else. So that suggests there's no need to rush, and this is reflected in the relaxed, swung rhythms of this piece. Despite its British title, this music has a strong feeling of the Blues, a genre of jazz that originated from African Americans in the Deep South of the USA towards the end of the 19th century.

Ned Bennett is a saxophonist and composer, and has produced many educational music books for Faber Music.

Grey Secrets

No. 2 from *Colour Studies*

Jeffery Wilson
(born 1957)

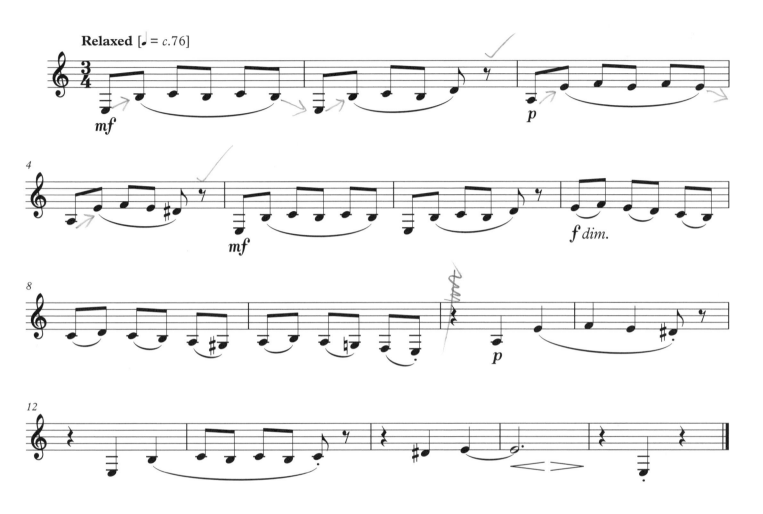

Sometimes in stories you're left guessing what the secret is: answering a riddle; cracking a code; venturing into a magical land beyond a secret door. From the very opening of this piece there's a feeling of mystery, and 'relaxed' legato phrasing helps create a sense of suspense. Perhaps the pairs of quavers in bars 7–9 are footsteps: they start loud but grow fainter and fainter, as if you're following them down a hidden stairwell. But where does it lead to? It's a secret!

Jeffery Wilson is a Professor of Composition at Junior Guildhall, and a visiting lecturer in Jazz and Improvisation at the Royal Military School of Music.

C:3

Eckington Stomp

No. 12 from *uTunes*

Martin Yates
(born 1954)

Eckington is a town in North East Derbyshire, near Sheffield and South Yorkshire. Some of the residents of Eckington like to have a good dance now and again, and that's what inspired this piece. In music, a stomp is a jazzy dance marked by stomping (or stamping) your foot down. Here the movements of the Eckington dancers are indicated by the accented notes – you will notice that some are short, and some are long. **In the exam you should play the quavers straight.**

Martin Yates is a British conductor, composer and orchestrator whose recent work has focused on film, symphonic wind band and brass band.

AB 3858